D0299278

SPACE CHASE

Steve Barlow and Steve Skidmore

Illustrated by Santy Gutiérrez

LONDON•SYDNEY

Franklin Watts
First published in Great Britain in 2019 by The Watts Publishing Group

Credits
Series Editor: Adrian Cole
Project Editor: Katie Woolley
Consultant: Jackie Hamley
Designer: Cathryn Gilbert
Illustrations: Santiago Gutiérrez

HB ISBN 978 1 4451 5892 1
PB ISBN 978 1 4451 5891 4
Library ebook ISBN 978 1 4451 5890 7

Printed in China.

Franklin Watts
An imprint of
Hachette Children's Group
Part of The Watts Publishing Group
Carmelite House
50 Victoria Embankment
London EC4Y 0DZ

An Hachette UK Company
www.hachette.co.uk

www.franklinwatts.co.uk

THE BADDIES

Lord and Lady Evil

Dr Y

They want to rule the galaxy.

THE GOODIES

Boo Hoo Jet Tip

They want to stop them.

We can hide on this planet.

DINER
They have GiFi! I can check Facebeing.
Instadroid!
Spacechat!
GI FI

Look at this!
What?

WANTED
DEAD OR ALIVE
REWARD

Every baddie in the galaxy will be after us!
They'll never find us here...

HOV-2
POTTY
They've found us!

Jet, Tip and Boo Hoo were knocked off their seats.

Jet pointed at the distant ship.

“It’s coming back!”

“We have to hide!” moaned Tip.

Boo Hoo pointed to a fancy dress store. “In there!”

01
POTTY

Jet groaned.

"It's Butt Hedd! One of the scariest baddies in the whole galaxy!"

What do we do?
Shh! I'm listening.

"I've followed the space cadets," reported Butt Hedd, "but they're hiding – I can't find them."

Lord Evil's voice crackled from the radio. "I'll send Dr Y. They won't escape his Find-o-Matic detector."

"Fine," agreed Butt Hedd. "What does Dr Y look like?"

"He's got three heads. You can't miss him."

Dr Y will find us for sure!
Squeak!
Are you a man or a mouse?

Jet held up a large white lab coat. "We have everything we need right here. But we'll have to be quick!"

Hi!
Yo!
Hello!
What the...?

Are you Dr Y?

Yep!
Sure am!
That's me!

Is that your Find-o-Matic detector?
You bet!
Too right!
Watch this...

'Dr Y' stopped at a manhole cover. Jet pointed at it.

"The cadets are down there."

Are you sure?

Sure...
we're...
sure!
OOF!

Now, let's get away before the real Dr Y shows up...

As they raced back to *Shawn the Ship*,
Jet asked Tip, “Where is Boo Hoo?”
“He’s behind us,” said Tip.
Jet glanced back. “No, he isn’t! What’s
he up to?”

Ready to go?
Nearly...

Where is Boo Hoo?
Here I am!

Won't Butt Hedd follow us, Boo Hoo?
No. I clamped his ship.
Mister Hedd? I'm Dr Y...

Looks like Butt Hedd is kicking butt!
THE END